The Great Big Multicultural Pattern Book

**Written and illustrated by
Dan Grossmann**

Cover by Dan Grossmann

Copyright © 1993, Good Apple

ISBN No. 0-86653-726-0

Printing No. 987654321

Good Apple
1204 Buchanan St., Box 299
Carthage, IL 62321-0299

SIMON & SCHUSTER *A Paramount Communications Company*

Contents

GA1453

To the Teacher

The people and cultures of our world are as diverse and rich as the earth itself. Living together in harmony becomes more attainable when we can understand and respect these differences. *The Great Big Multicultural Pattern Book* is a valuable resource for teachers who want to acquaint their students with the many unique cultures of the world.

Each section of *The Great Big Multicultural Pattern Book* features a map of one of ten geographic regions and accompanying illustrations of the people who live there. While the line drawings of the places and faces of the world are simple enough for students to color and comprehend, they also provide a wealth of information about the biological and cultural heritage of each region.

The maps and illustrations in *The Great Big Multicultural Pattern Book* can be used for a variety of creative activities. Encourage students to use them in shape books, big books, collages and coloring books, or as paper bag puppets or report covers. Challenge students to learn more about cultural geography with map skill activities, flash cards, or games created from the pages of this book. Or use selected illustrations as bulletin board displays, stand-up figurines, or decorations on parent letters and other forms of classroom correspondence.

No matter how it is used, *The Great Big Multicultural Pattern Book* will prove to be a helpful addition to the resource collection of any classroom.

GA1448

NORTH AMERICA

1

GA1448

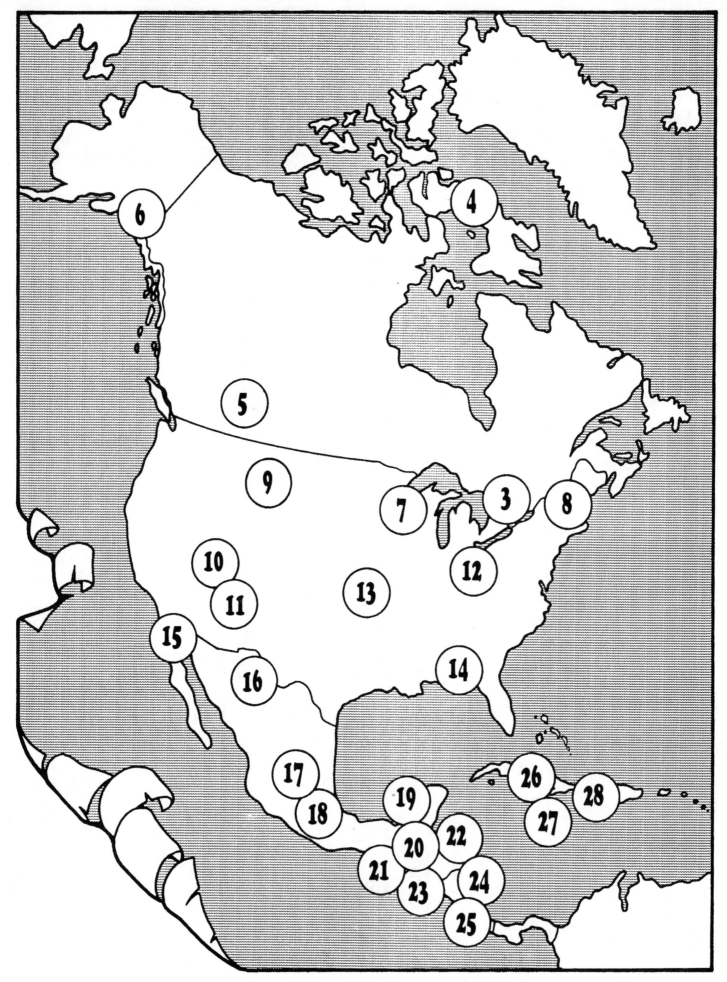

2

Canada

Canada's most popular sport

3

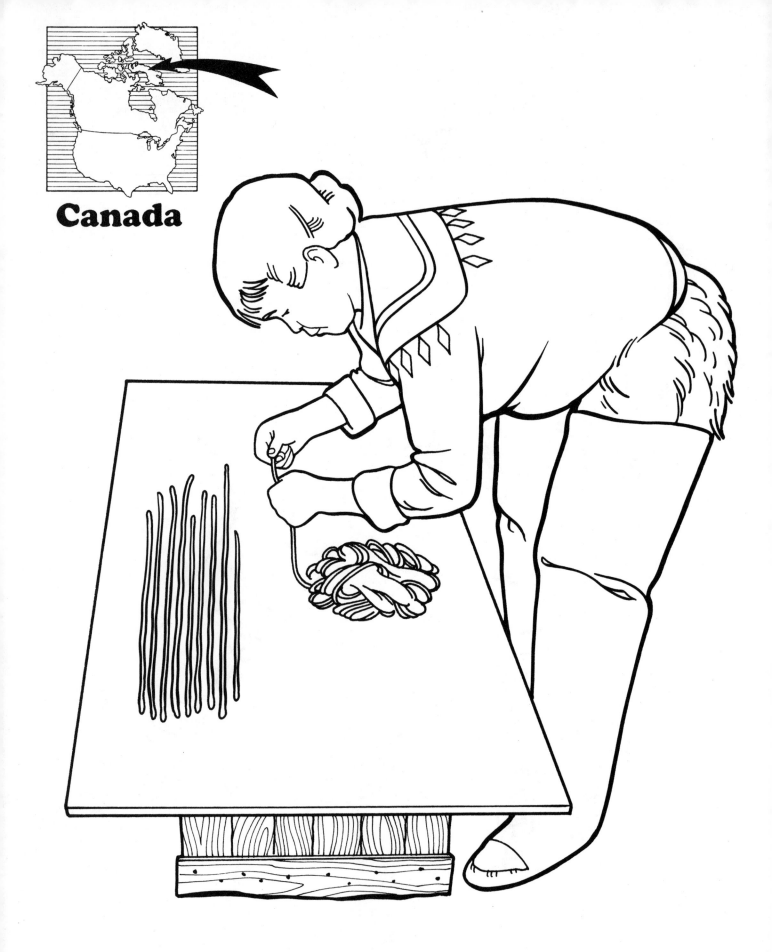

Canada

Inuit woman spreads narwhal sinew to dry

4

GA1448

Canada

Young buckaroo

5

GA1448

U.S.A.

Eskimo girl exhibits a caribou-hide mask

6

GA1448

U.S.A.

Milking lesson

7

U.S.A.

Sugaring in Vermont

8

U.S.A.

Young cowboy

GA1448

U.S.A.

Hopi maiden

10

GA1448

U.S.A.

Hopi buffalo dancer

11

GA1448

Amish mother and daughter

U.S.A.

GA1448

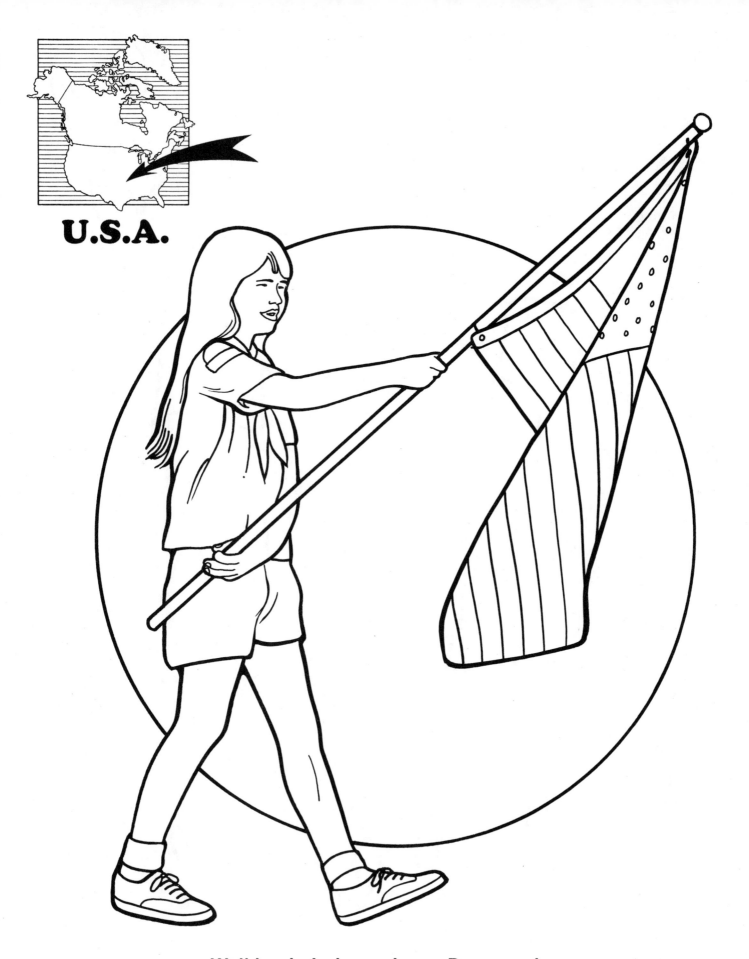

U.S.A.

Walking in Independence Day parade

13

U.S.A.

Two on two

14

GA1448

Mexico

After a day at the market

GA1448

Mexico

Basket merchant

16

GA1448

Mexico

Mexican girl

GA1448

Mexico

Breaking the piñata

GA1448

Mexico

Mexican Indian wearing a celebration costume

19

GA1448

Guatemala

Parrot seller

20

GA1448

Guatemala

Guatemalan Indians selling corn

21

GA1448

Honduras

Banana harvesters

GA1448

El Salvador

Drying coffee beans

23

Nicaragua

Young girl making corn tortillas

24

Costa Rica

Boruca Indians washing clothes

GA1448

Cuba

Tobacco field-worker

26

Jamaica

Jamaican fruit seller

27

ARCADIA
LMC

GA1448

Haiti

Haitian mother and child

GA1448

SOUTH AMERICA

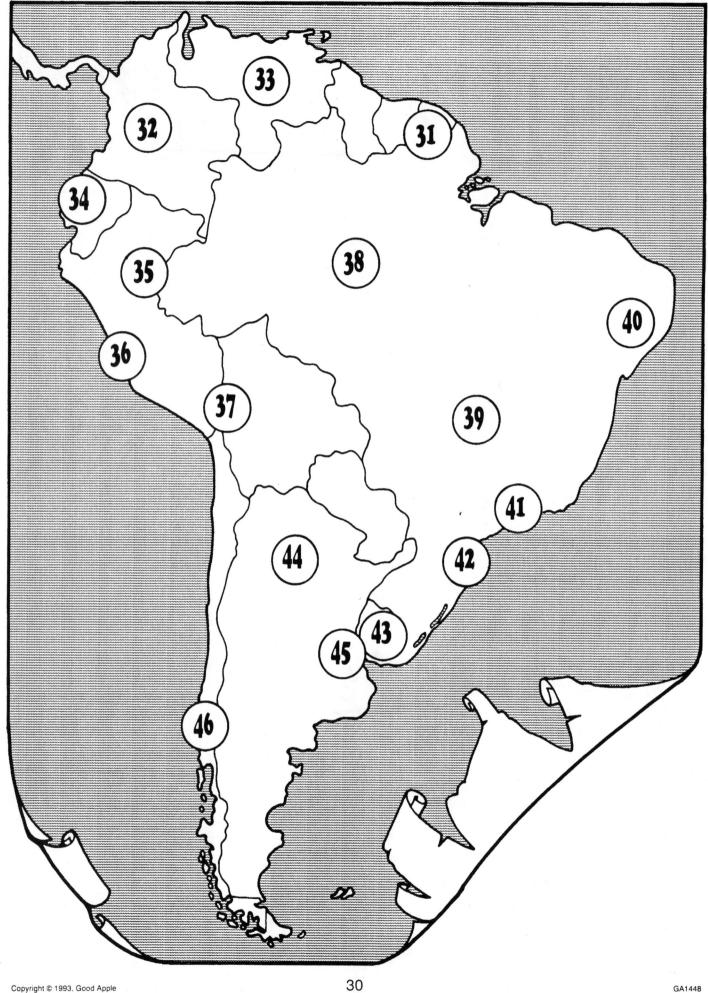

GA1448

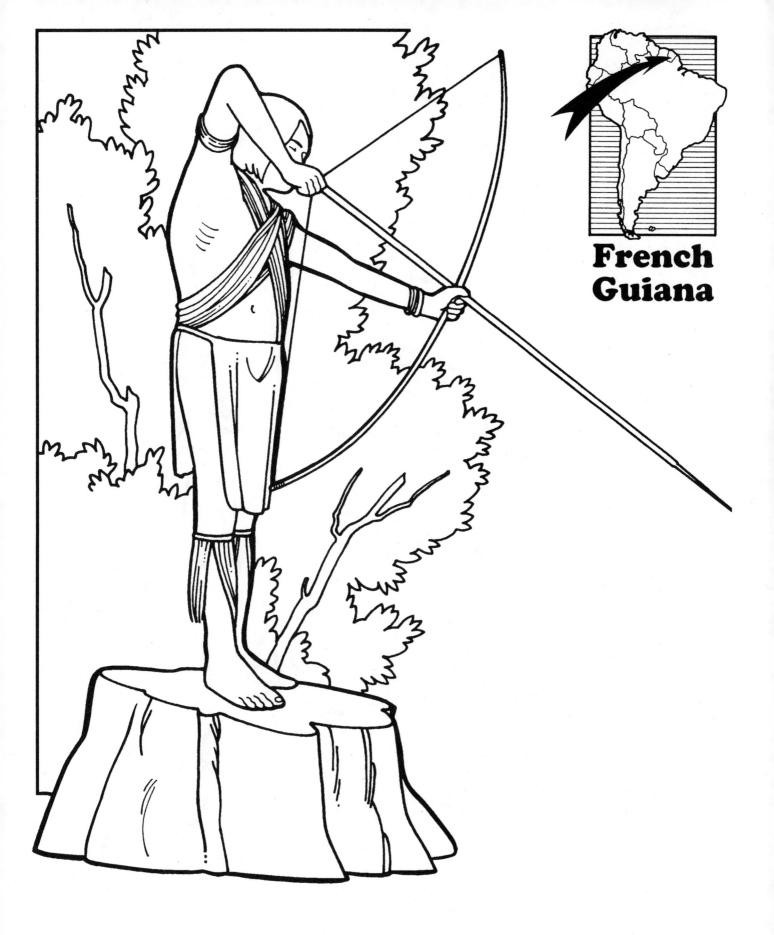

French Guiana

Oyana Indian bow fishing

GA1448

Colombia

Mestizo girl

32

GA1448

Venezuela

Yanomami Indians

GA1448

Ecuador

Ecuadorian Indian playing a rondador

34

GA1448

Peruvian marketplace

35

GA1448

Peru

Street fiddler

36

GA1448

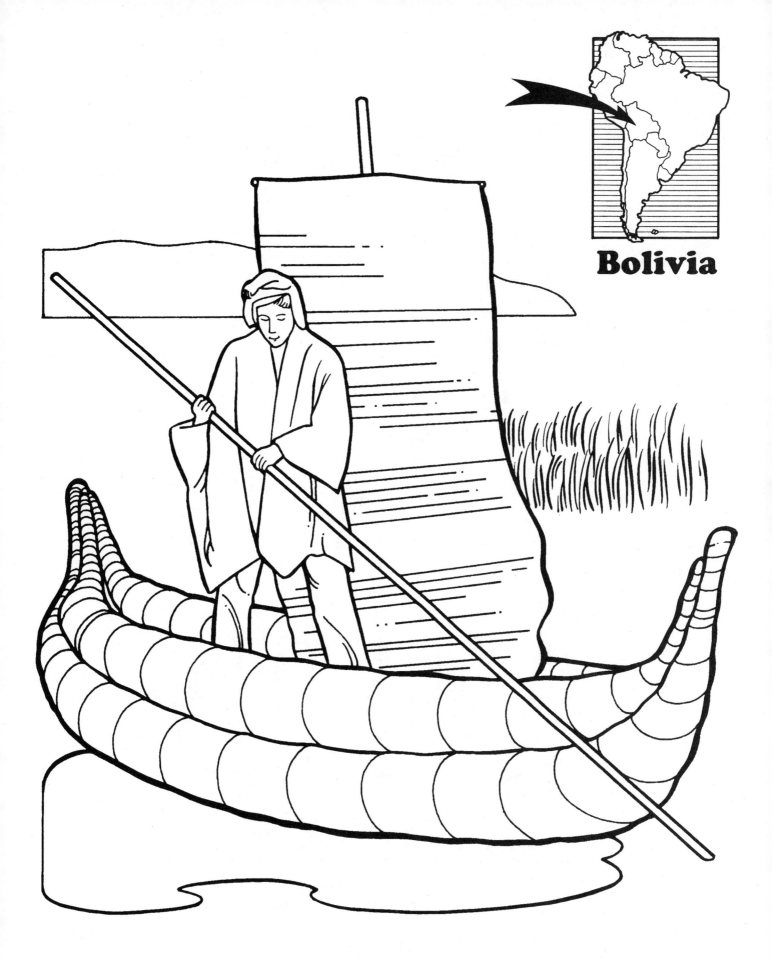

Bolivia

Reed boat on Lake Titicaca

GA1448

Brazil

Yagua Indian with blowgun

38

GA1448

Brazil

Cleaning coffee beans

GA1448

Brazil

Young girl gleaning sugarcane

40

Brazil

Mat maker

GA1448

Brazil

Celebrating carnival

42

Uruguay

Uruguayan rancher

GA1448

Argentina

Horseman of the pampas

44

GA1448

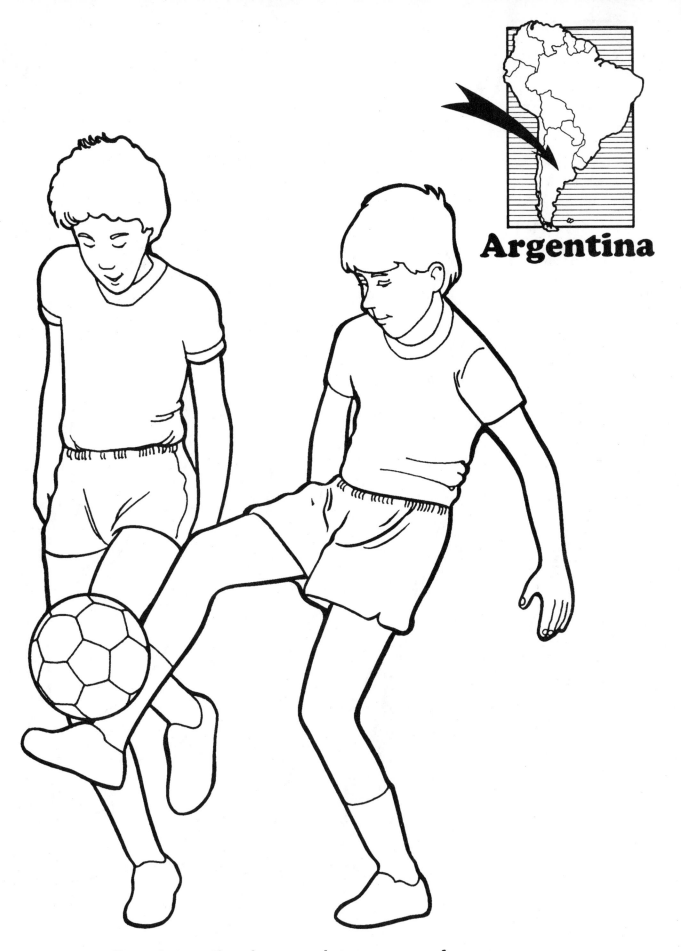

Two Argentine boys enjoy a game of soccer

45

GA1448

Araucanian Indian

46

GA1448

WESTERN EUROPE

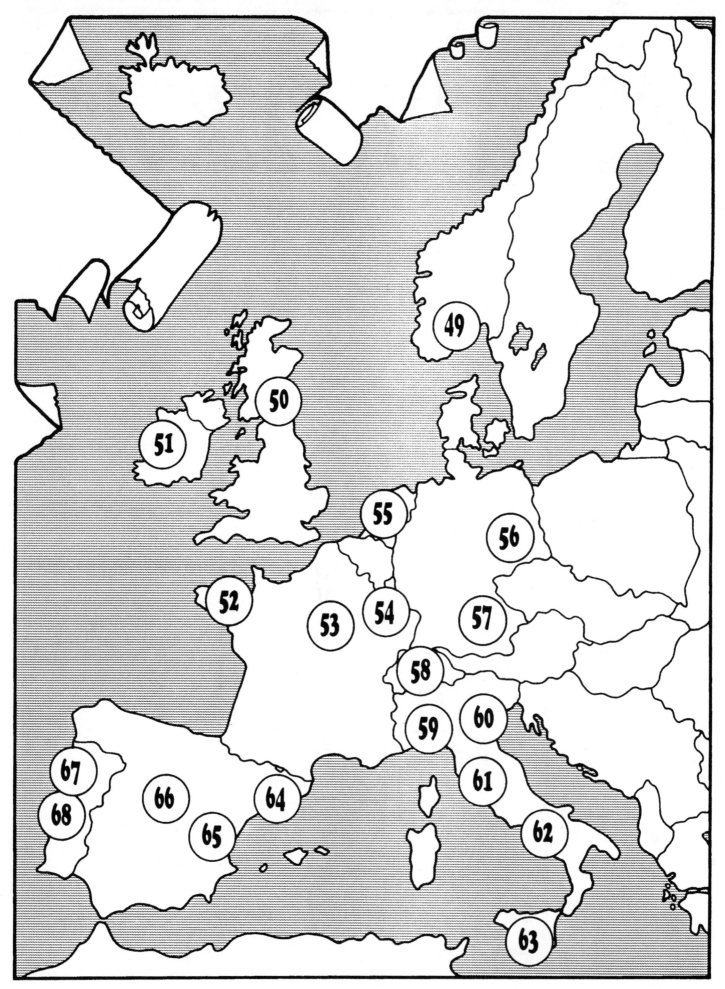

48

GA1448

Craftsman and son

Norway

49

GA1448

United Kingdom

Scotsman

50

GA1448

Ireland

Collecting peat fuel

51

GA1448

France

Breton woman gathers kelp

GA1448

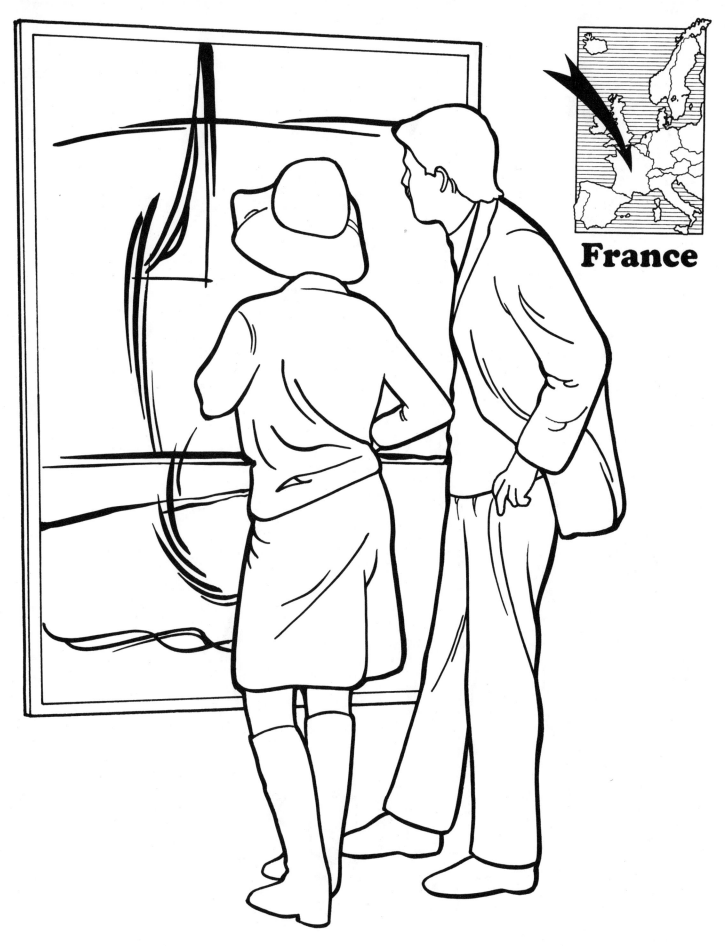

France

Art lovers

53

France

Alsatian girl holding a kugelhof cake

54

GA1448

Netherlands

Traditional Dutch dress

55

Germany

Two girls in the traditional dress of their hometown

56

GA1448

Germany

Bavarian resting place

GA1448

Switzerland

Alpenhorns

58

GA1448

Italy

Traditional Sicilian love dance

59

GA1448

Italy

Venetian gondola

60

Italy

Italian farmer rides home

GA1448

Italy

Italian shepherd watches his sheep

62

GA1448

Italy

Young Sicilian woman

63

Spain

Spanish guitarist with Andalusian dancer

64

GA1448

Spain

Grape harvest

65

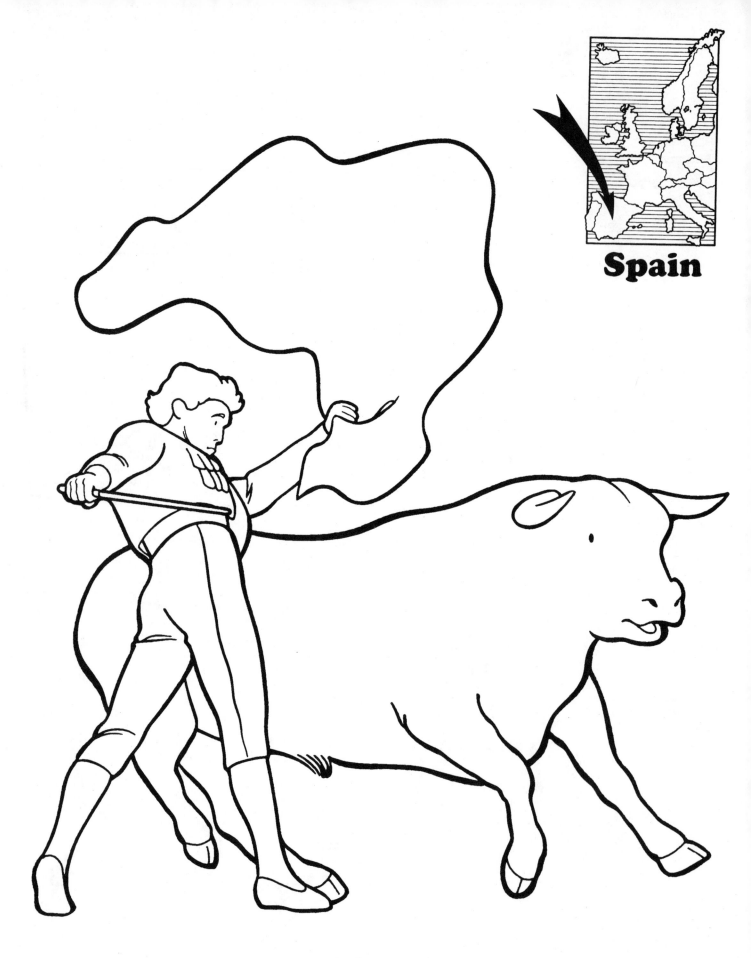

Spain

Bullfight

66

Portugal

Village hydrant

67

GA1448

Portugal

Sorting fish

68

EASTERN EUROPE

69

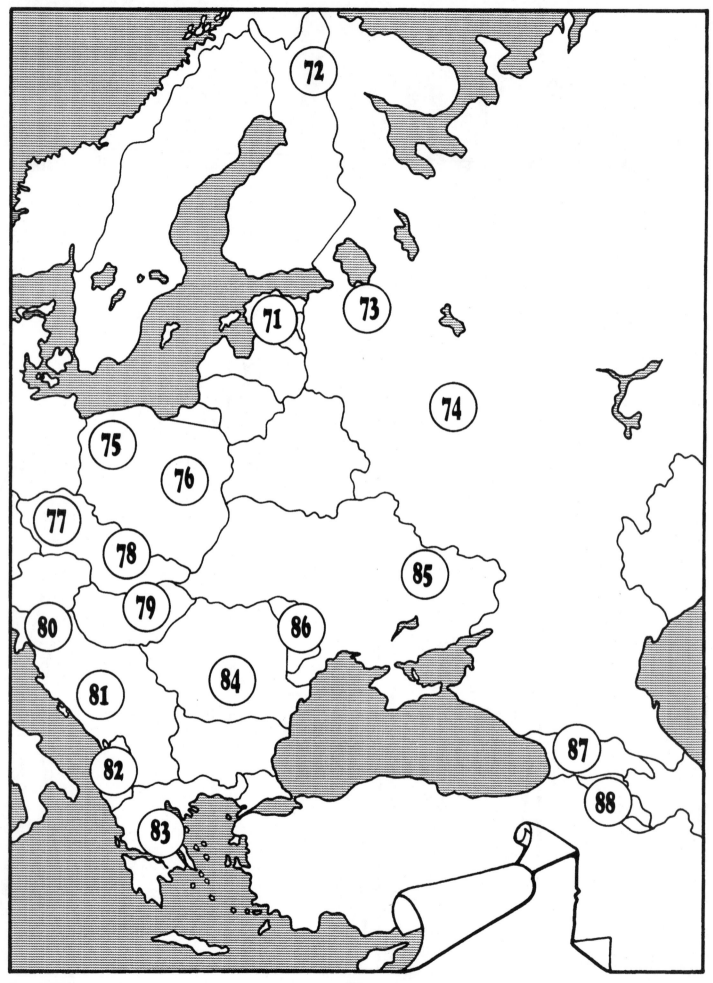

70

GA1448

Estonia

Estonian folk dance

71

GA1448

Finland

Laplanders gathering wood for fuel

72

GA1448

Russia

Russian ballet

73

Russia

Street repair crew

GA1448

Poland

Gathering household fuel

75

GA1448

Poland

To the harvest fields

GA1448

Czechoslovakia

Women field-workers

Czechoslovakia

Slovakian harvest dance

78

GA1448

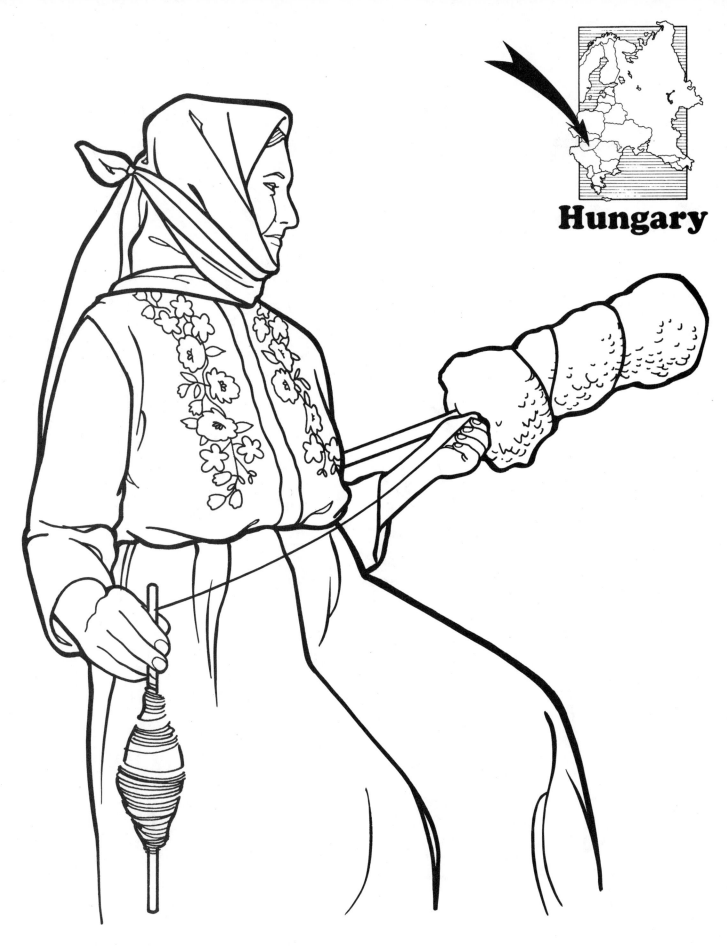

Hungary

Hand-spinning wool

GA1448

Yugoslavia

Slovenian farmer repairing his rake

80

Yugoslavia

Earnest discussion

81

GA1448

Albania

Albanian women discuss local news

82

GA1448

Greek shepherd

83

GA1448

Romania

Gypsy woman

GA1448

Ukraine

Ukrainian schoolgirl

85

Moldova

Moldovian woman harvesting grapes

86

Georgian plays his lute

87

GA1448

Armenia

Armenian farm worker

GA1448

NORTH AFRICA

89

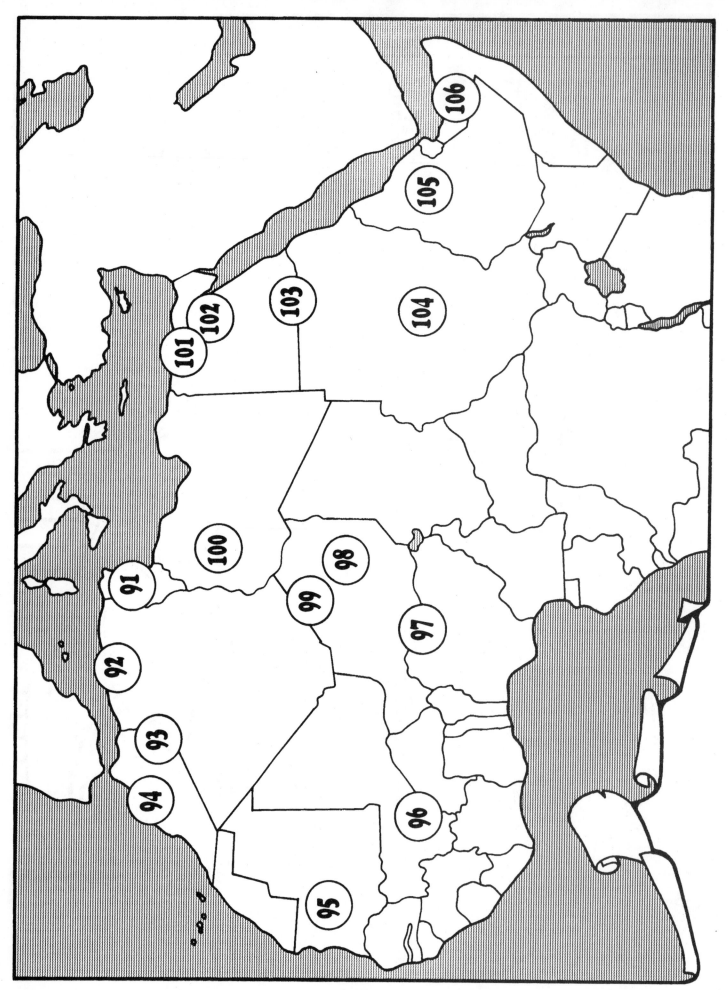

GA1448

Tunisia

Palace guard

91

Algeria

Talking business

GA1448

Morocco

Making bread

93

Morocco

Berber children

GA1448

Mauritania

Moorish woman

GA1448

Mali

Winnowing corn in the wind

GA1448

Hausa man dressed for a Muslim festival

GA1448

Niger

Wodaabe woman enjoys a midday tea break

98

GA1448

Niger

Fetching water for their cattle

GA1448

Libya

Singing legends on the imzad

GA1448

Egypt

Egyptian taxi

Egypt

Drawing water

102

Coptic teacher and pupil

GA1448

Sudan

Nubian woman

104

GA1448

Ethiopia

Beni Amer mother and child

105

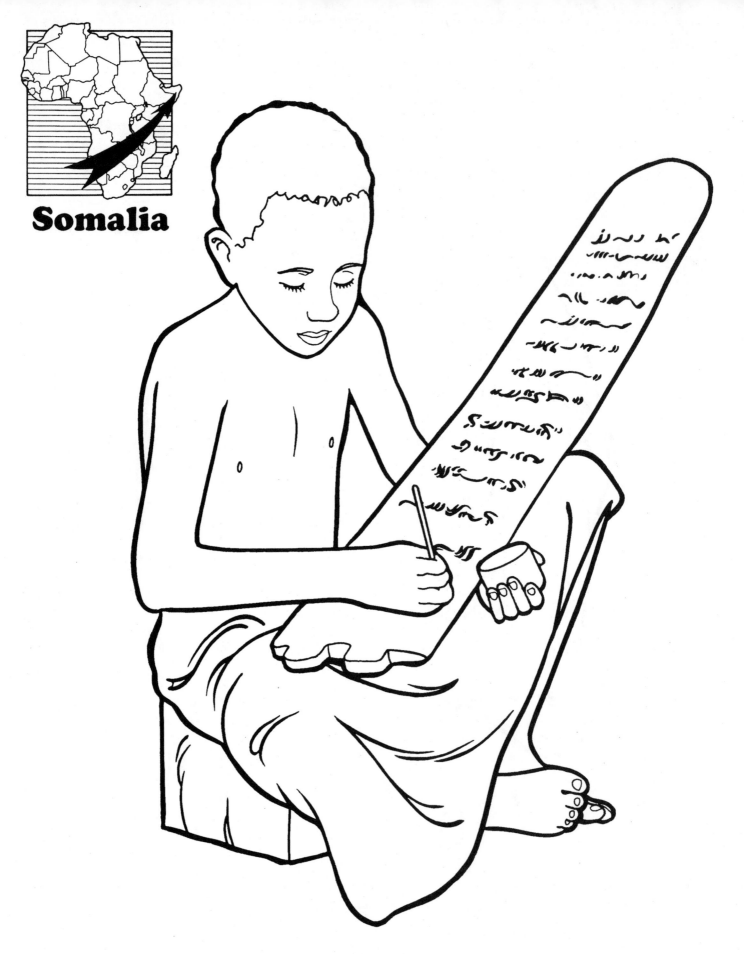

Somali boy practices his Arabic.

106

GA1448

SOUTH AND CENTRAL
AFRICA

107

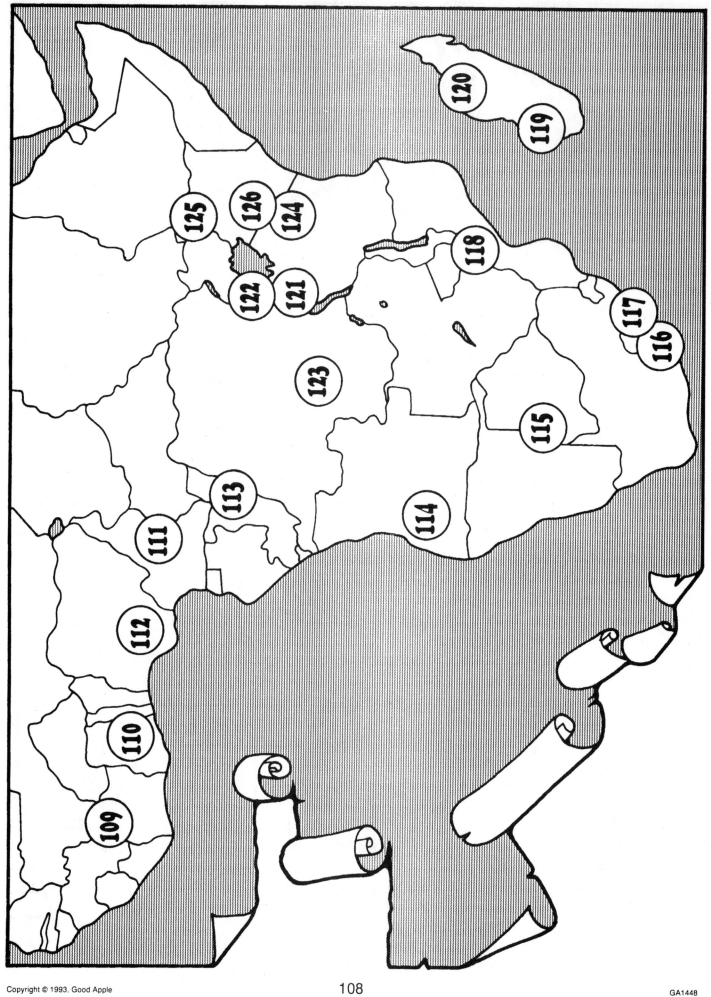

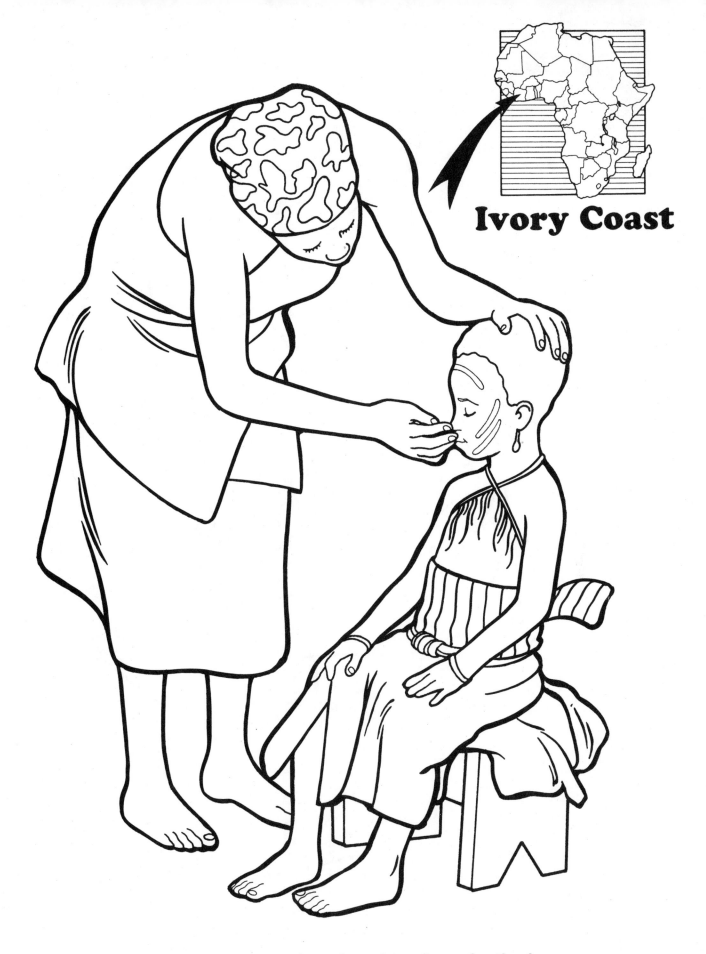

Ivory Coast

Mother makes up her daughter for a festival

GA1448

Ghana

Fishing with net in a tree bark canoe

GA1448

Cameroon

Weaver dyeing his threads

GA1448

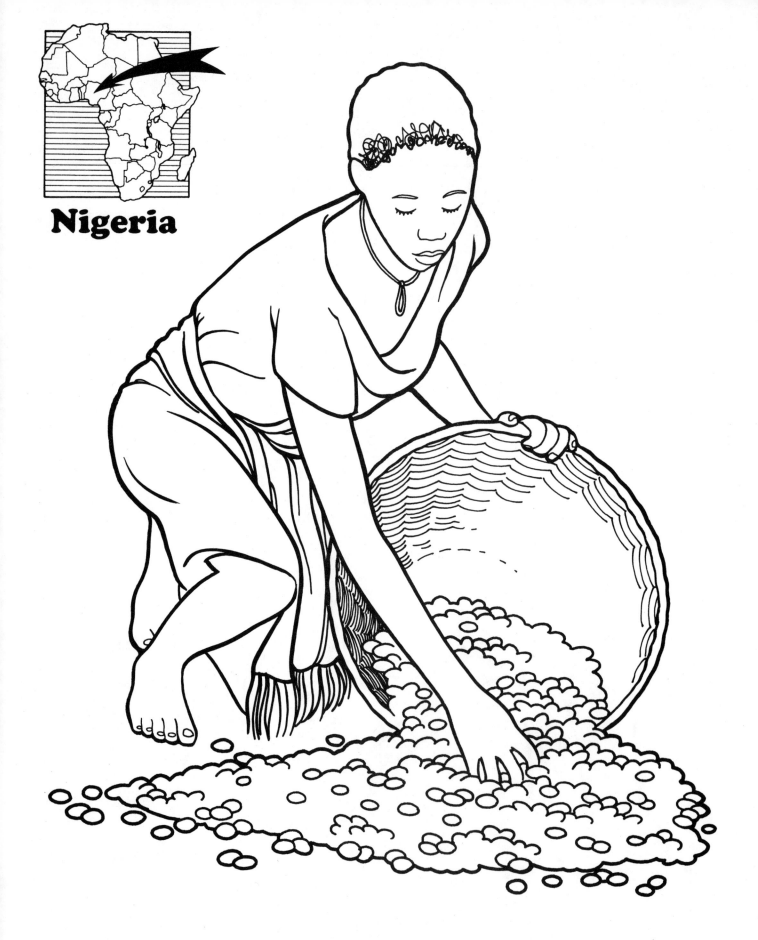

Nigeria

Collecting palm oil nuts

GA1448

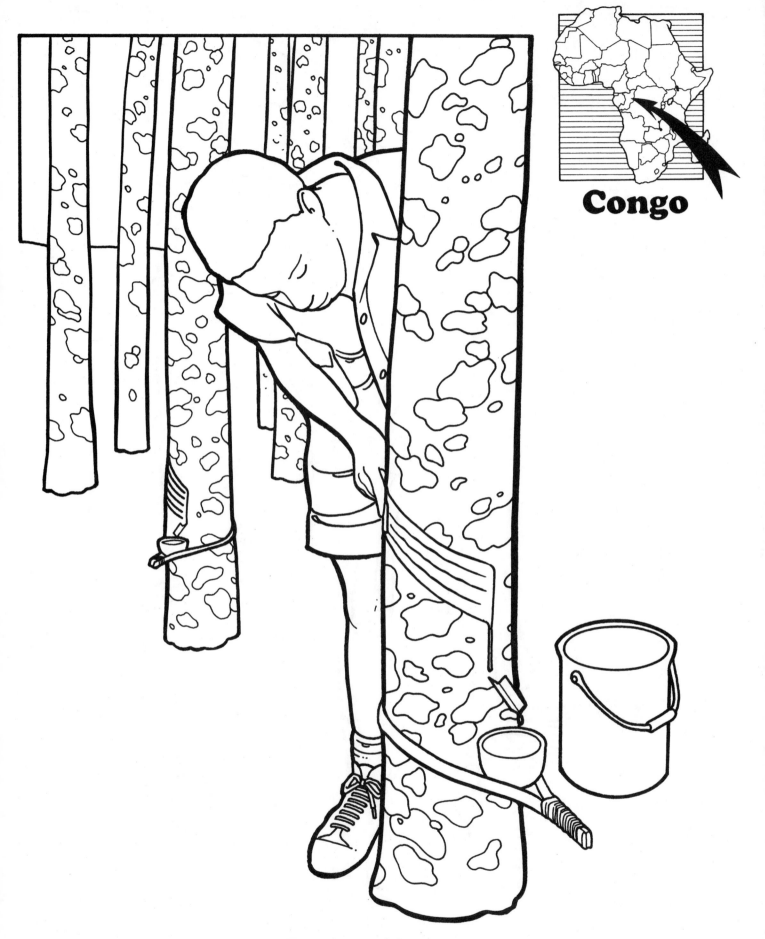

Congo

Tapping rubber trees

Angola

Crushing grain

GA1448

Bushman drinks from an ostrich egg container

Mpondo woman

116

GA1448

Transkei

Transkei

Gcaleka woman

GA1448

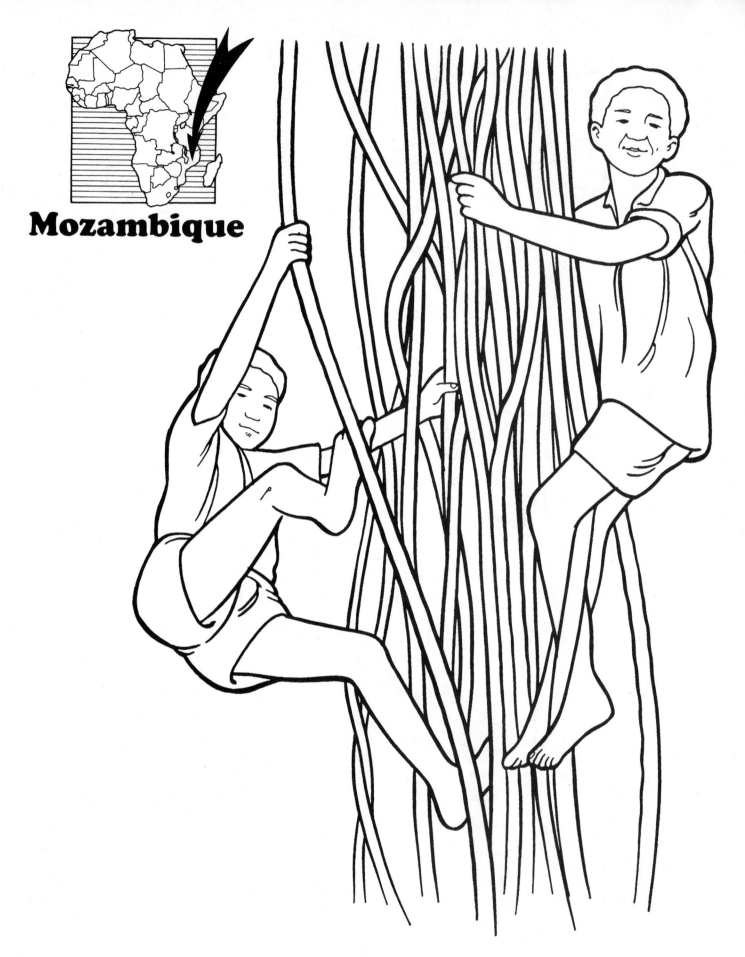

Mozambique

Playing in the roots of a camoe tree

GA1448

Madagascar

Threshing rice

GA1448

Madagascar

Cart ride to market

120

GA1448

Rwanda

Tutsi dance

121

GA1448

Rwanda

Tutsi woman

122

GA1448

Zaire

Math class

123

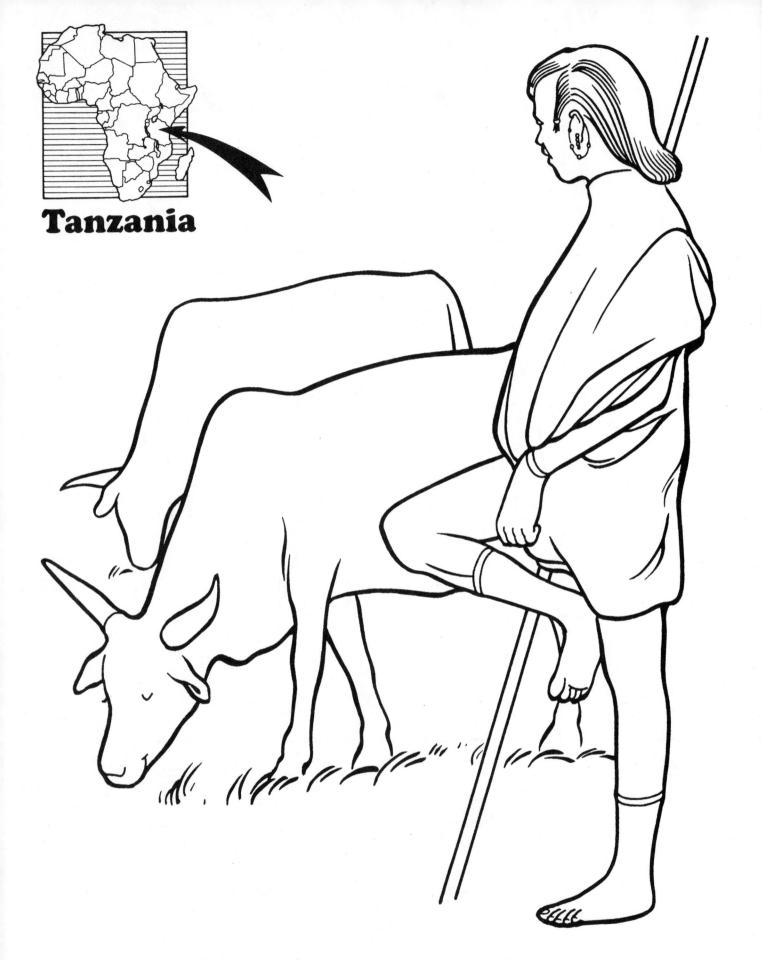

Tanzania

Characteristic stance of a Masai herdsman

124

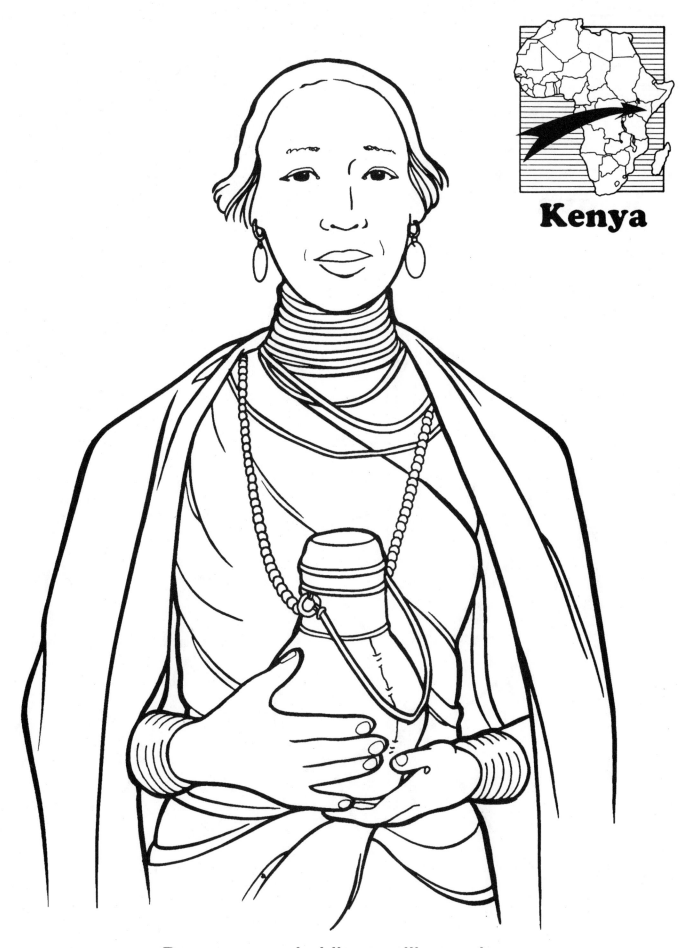

Kenya

Boran woman holding a milk gourd

125

Kenya

Masai bride dressed for her wedding

126

GA1448

SOUTHWEST ASIA

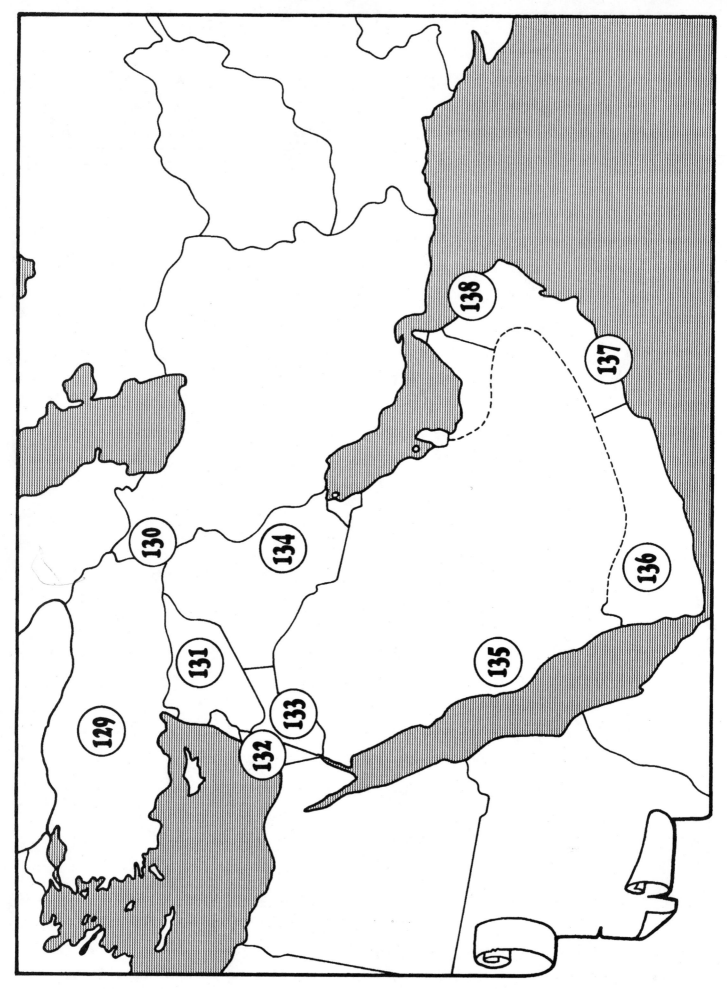

Turkey

Anatolian farmer threshing wheat

129

GA1448

Iran

Kurdish mother and child

130

GA1448

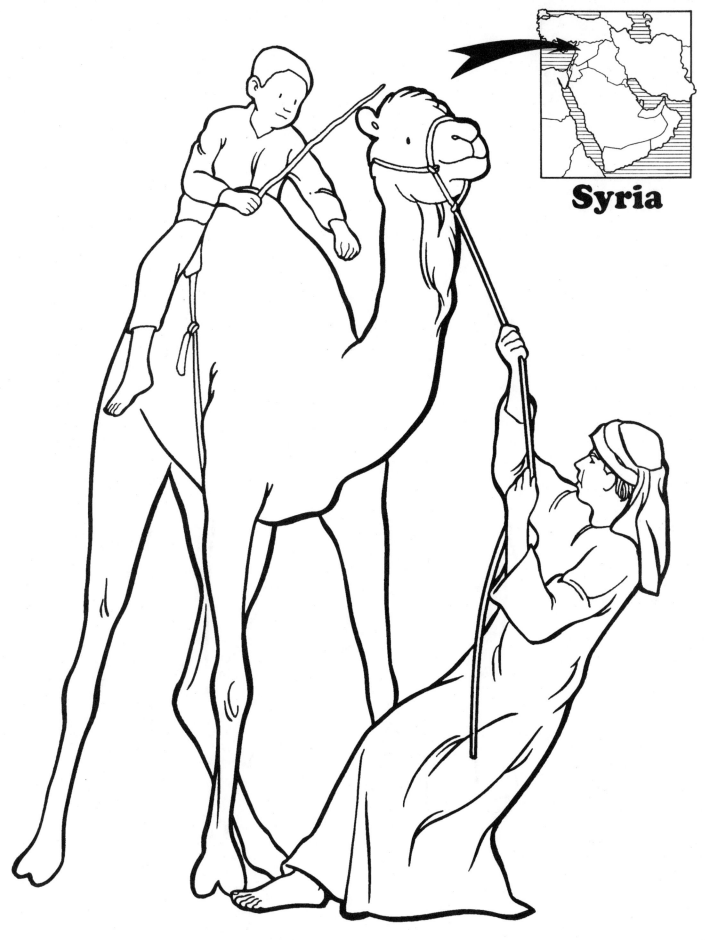

Syria

Stubborn transportation

GA1448

Israel

Father and son at the Western Wall

Jordan

Musician playing the single string rabab

133

Iraq

Tea break for Iraqi fruit vendor

134

Saudi Arabia

Saudi boy displays his dates

GA1448

Yemen

Bedouins of Yemen

136

Oman

Fisherman mending his nets

Oman

Camel gets a bath

138

SOUTH AND CENTRAL ASIA

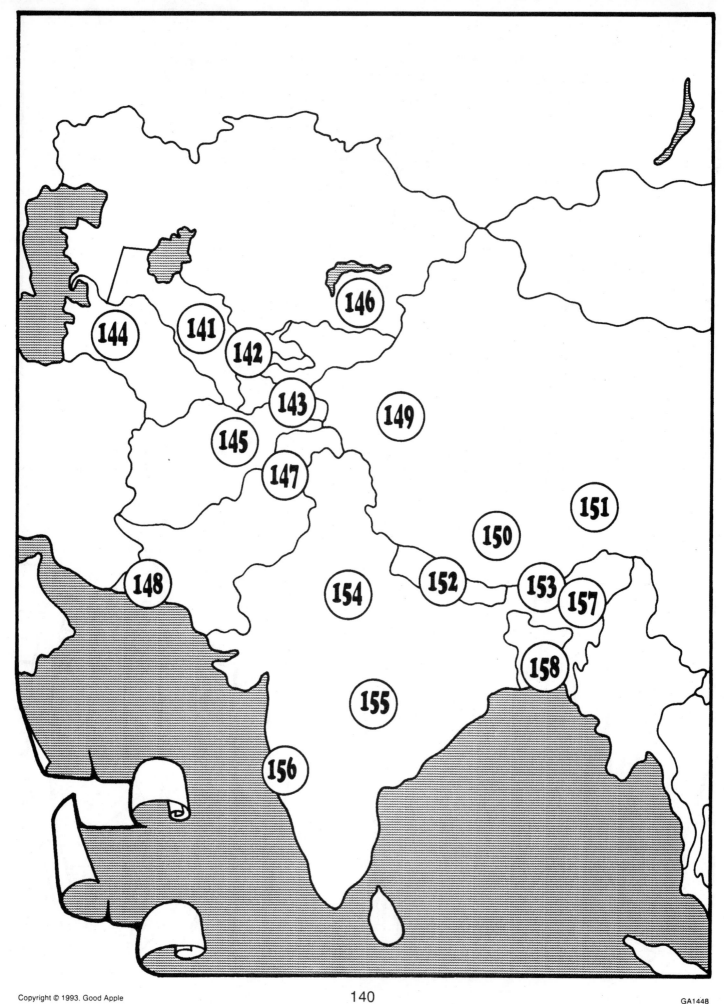

Uzbekistan

Loading the cotton harvest

141

Uzbekistan

Uzbek field-worker

142

Tajikistan

Cooking at an open-air bazaar

GA1448

Turkmenistan

Turkmen woman prepares sheepskins for market

GA1448

Afghanistan

Afghan women completely veiled by the shadri

145

Kazakhstan

Midday meal of bread and tea

GA1448

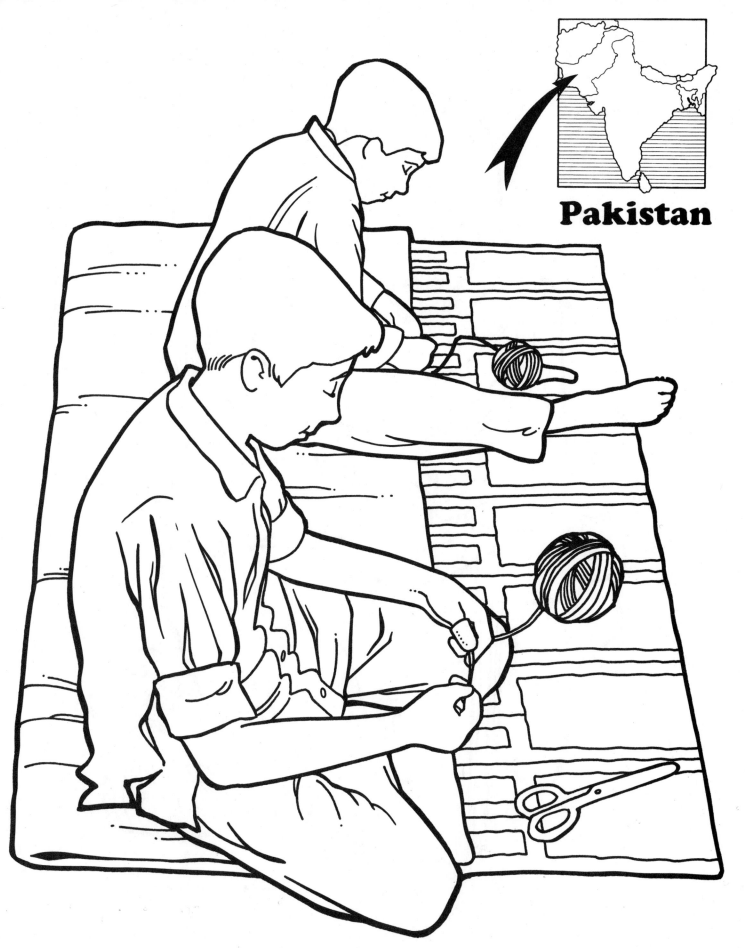

Pakistan

Young Pakistani rug weavers

147

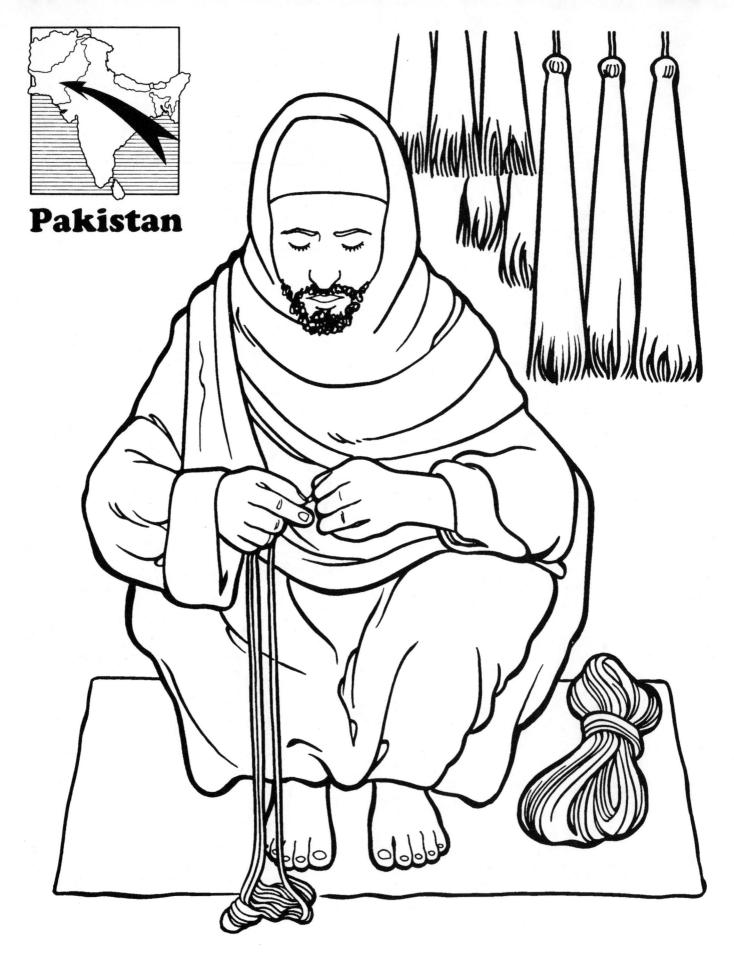

Pakistan

Tassel maker

Making buttered tea, a favorite drink in Tibet

149

GA1448

Tibet

Yak ride

GA1448

Tibet

Cutting grass

GA1448

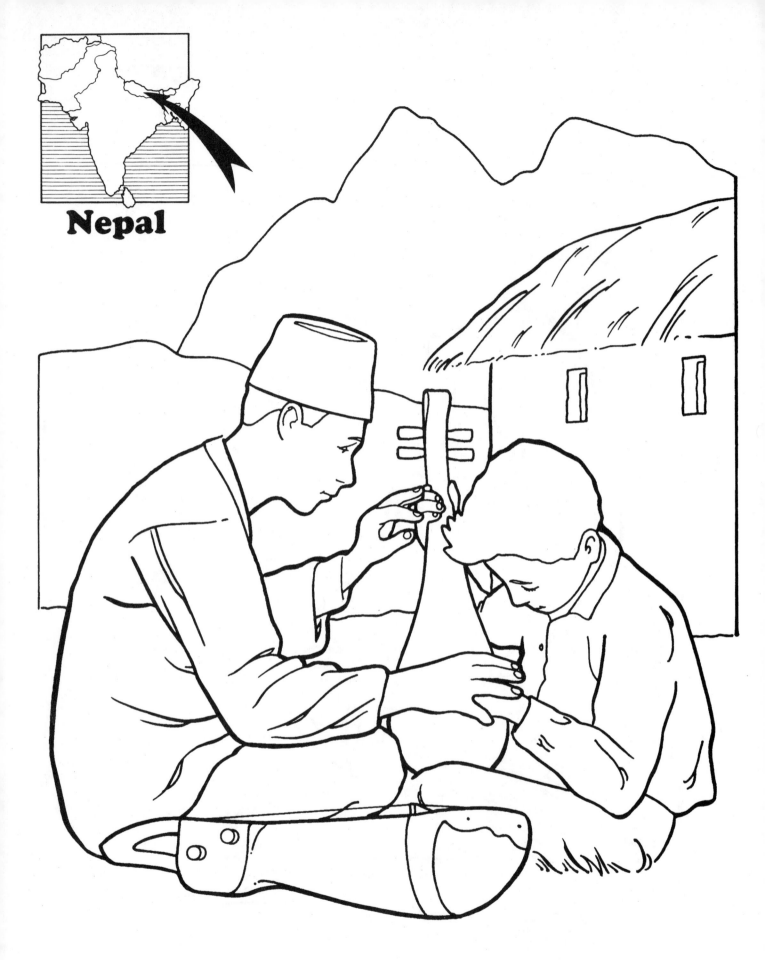

Nepal

Music lessons

152

GA1448

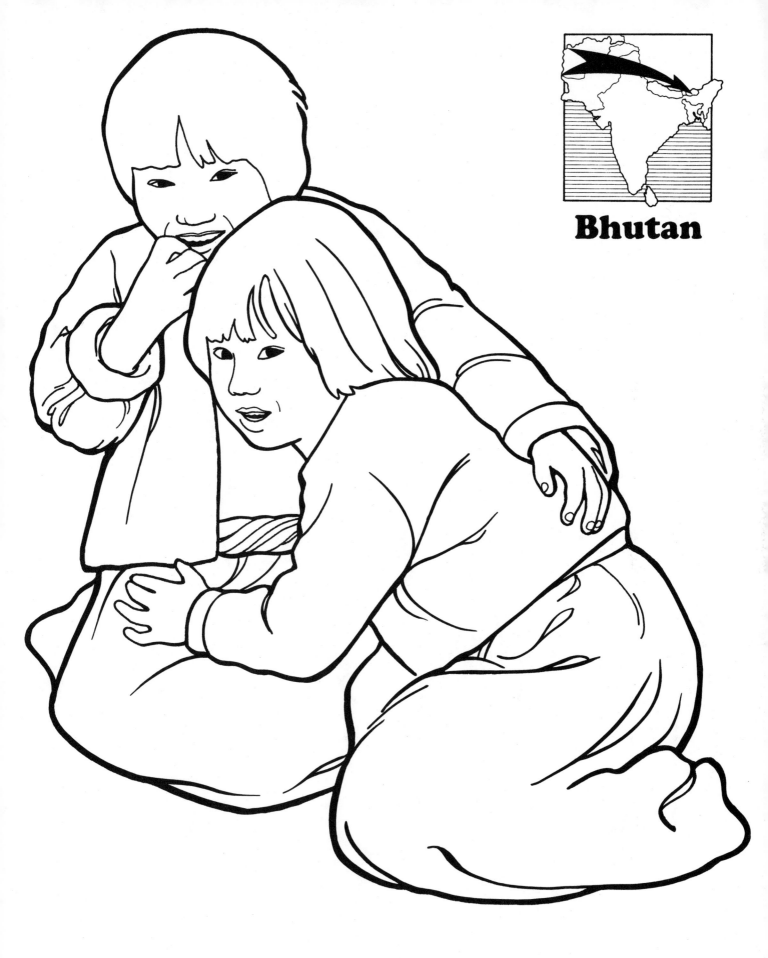

Bhutan

Bhutanese children

GA1448

India

Making bricks

154

GA1448

Playing the tabla drums

India

GA1448

Indian street dentist at work

156

GA1448

An Indian elephant moves heavy logs

GA1448

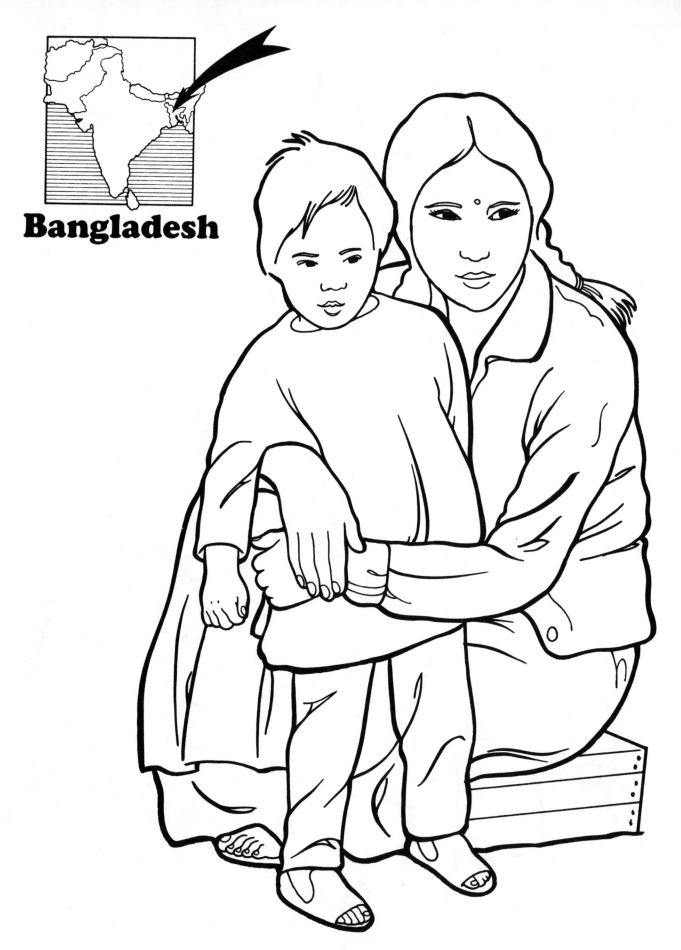

Bangladesh

Mother and child

158

GA1448

EAST AND SOUTHEAST ASIA

159

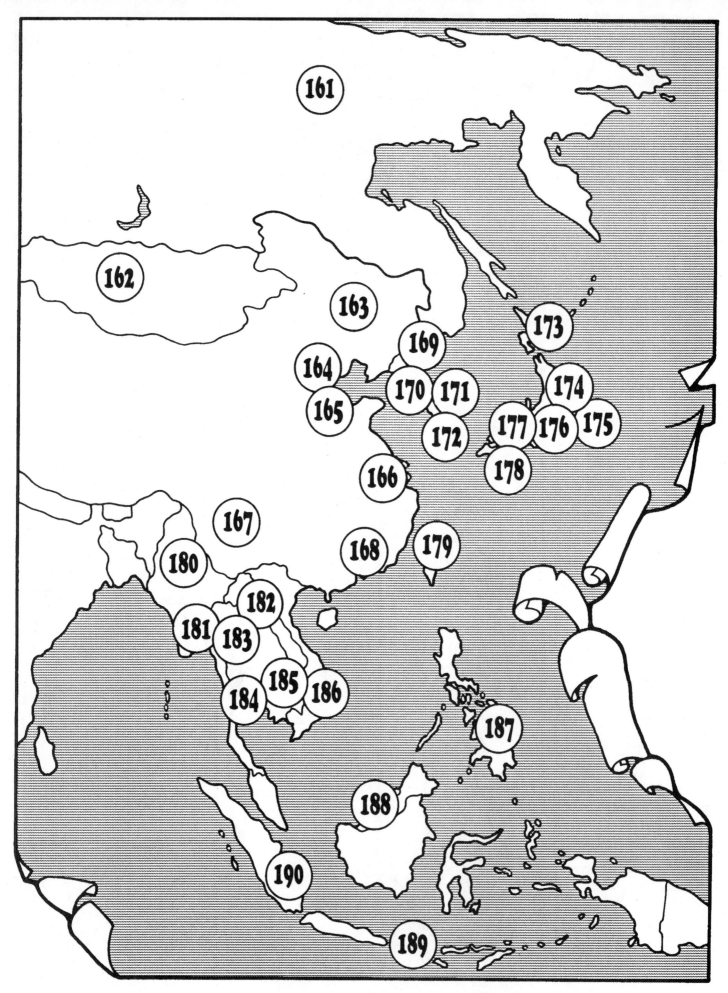

160

GA1448

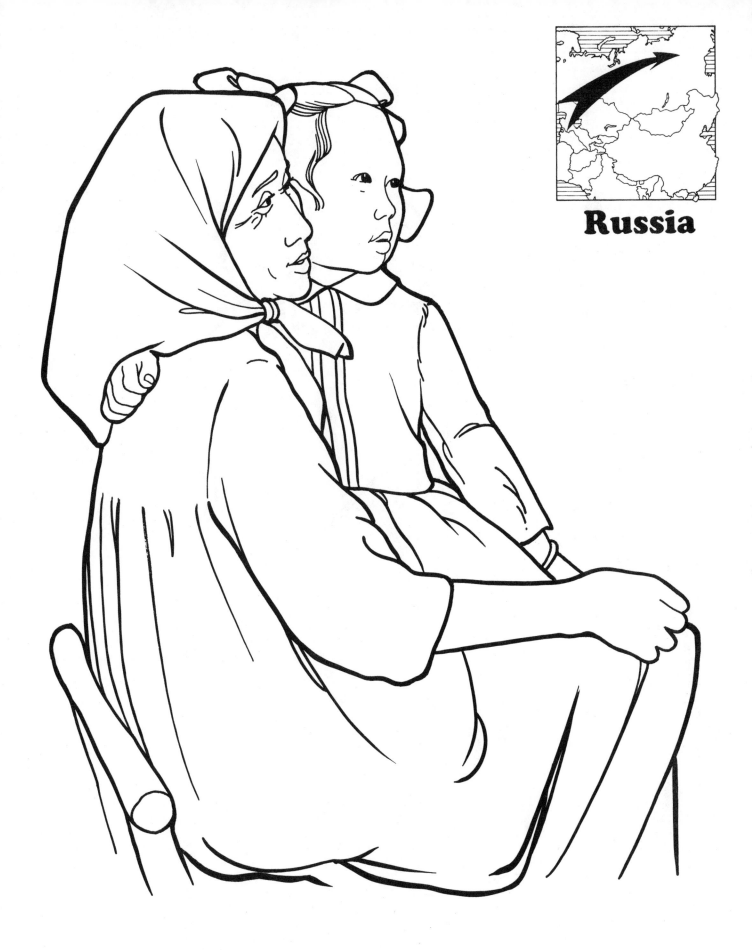

Russia

Yakut woman with her granddaughter

Mongolia

Mongolian herdsmen pack their yak

162

Student learning math with an abacus

GA1448

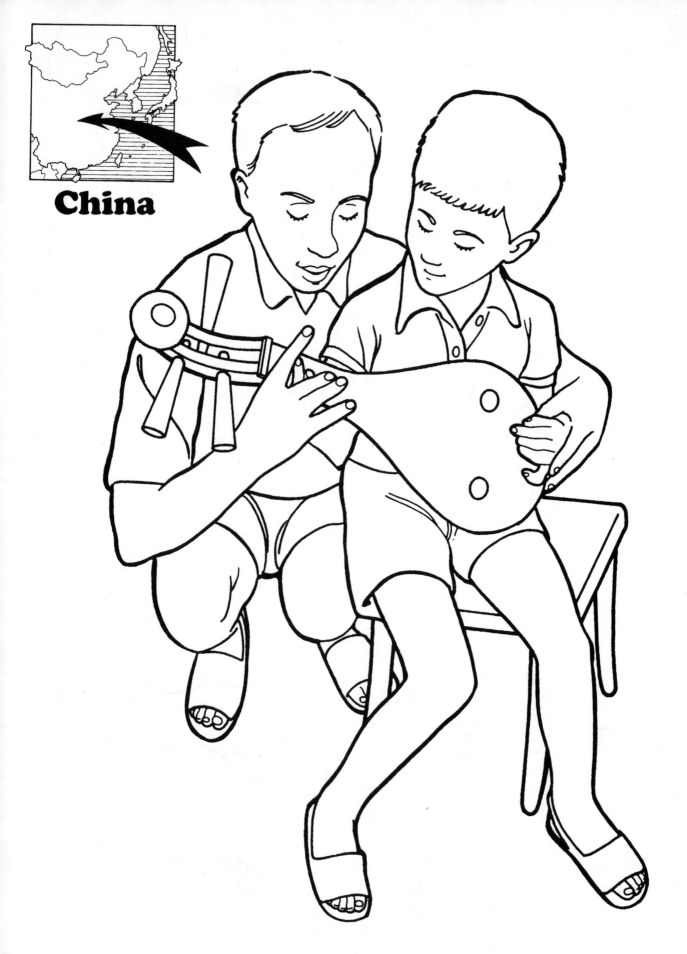

China

Father teaches his son

164

GA1448

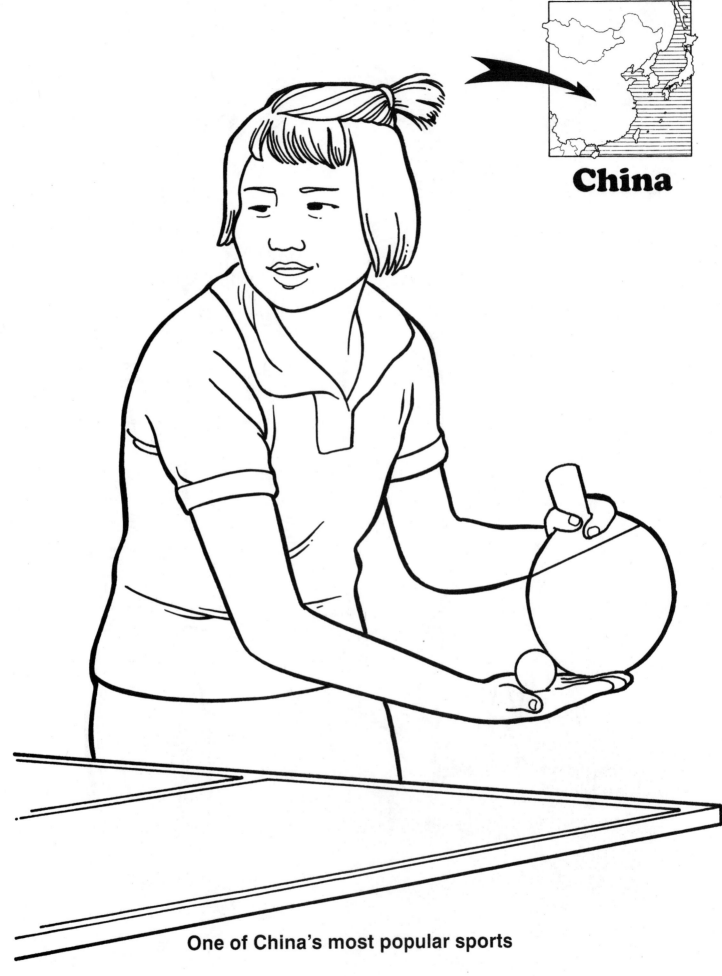

China

One of China's most popular sports

165

China

Chinese basket maker on his way to market

166

China

Mother and child

GA1448

China

Chinese junk

GA1448

Farmer carrying his wheat

GA1448

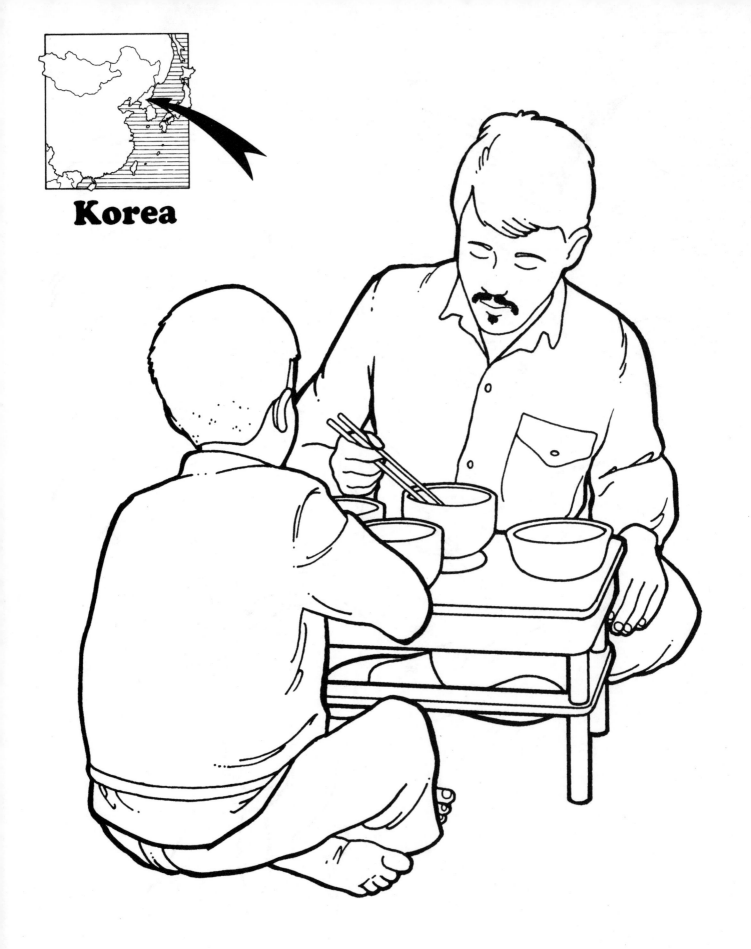

Korea

Father and son enjoying a meal

170

GA1448

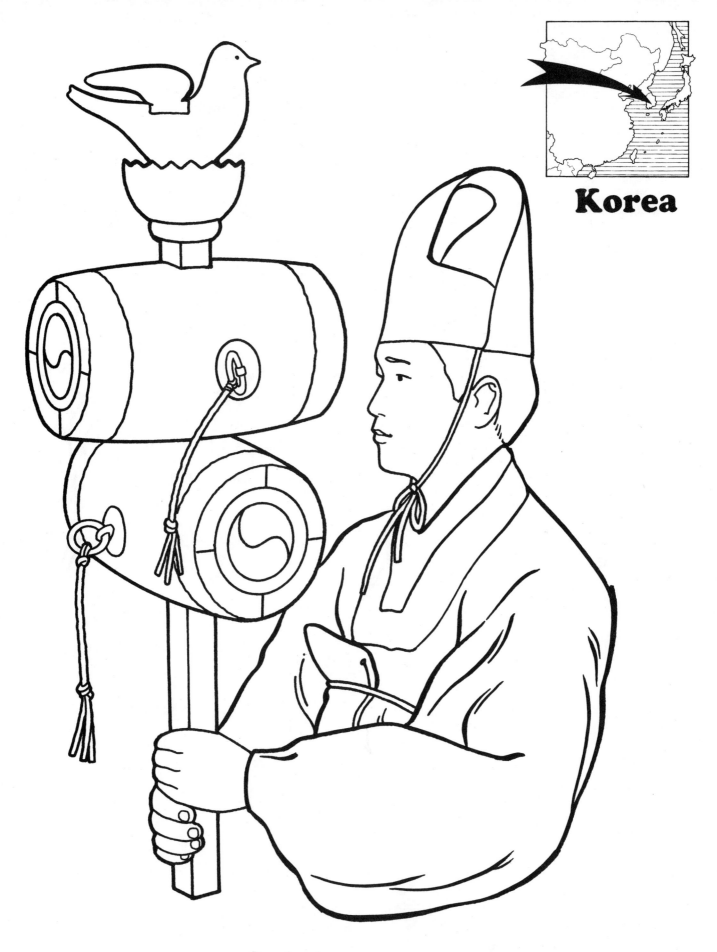

Korea

Confucian ceremony

GA1448

Korea

Flying a kite

172

GA1448

Picking tender tea leaves

173

GA1448

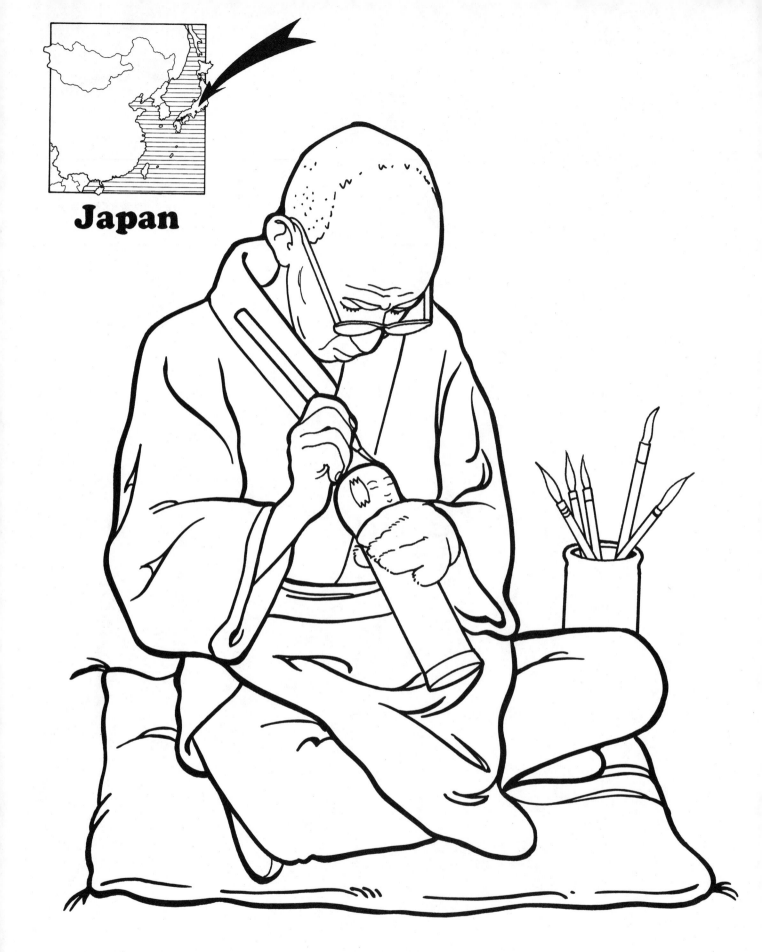

Japan

Doll maker

174

Japan

Ceremonial tea

GA1448

Japan

Off to school

176

GA1448

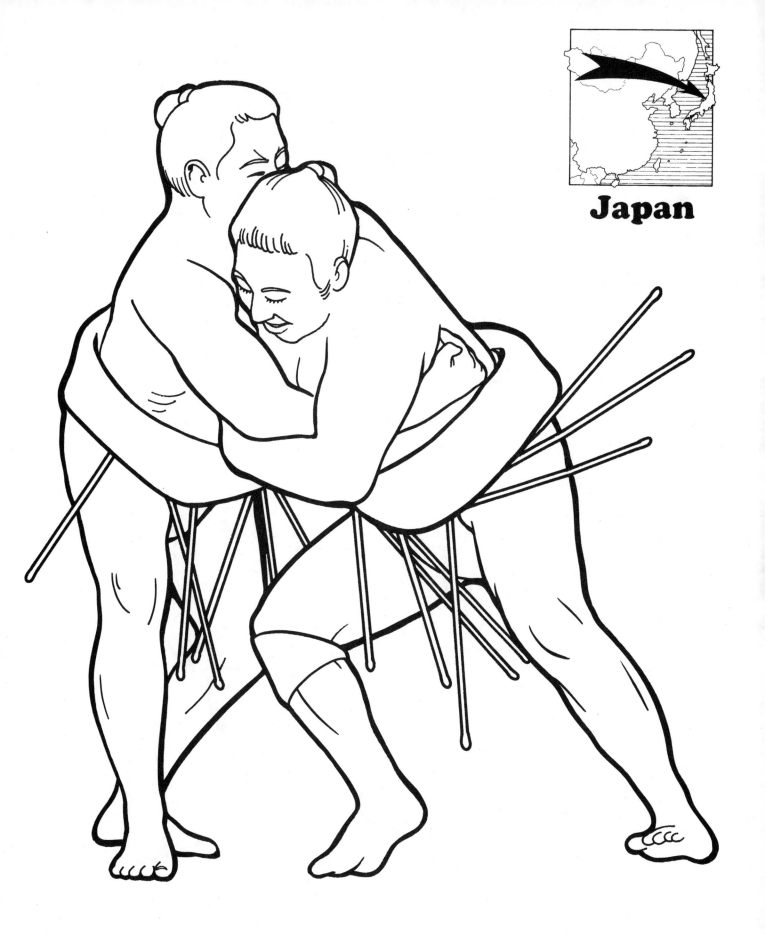

Japan

Sumo wrestlers

177

GA1448

Japan

Woman dressed in a traditional kimono

GA1448

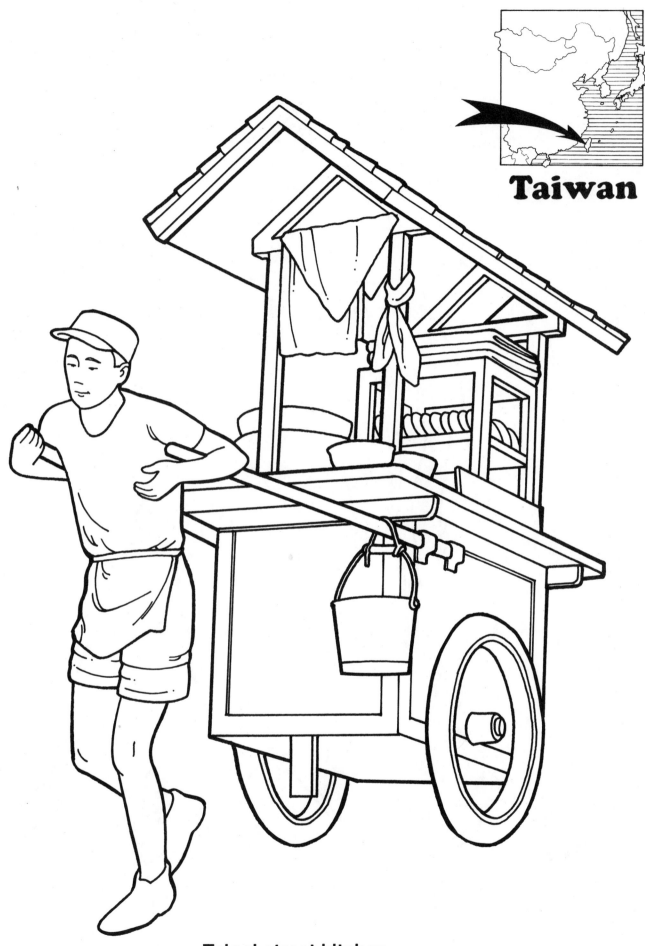

Taiwan

Taipei street kitchen

Burma

Karen woman in Burmese royal court dress

180

GA1448

Burma

Teacher with his pupils

GA1448

Laos

Meo woman of Laos

GA1448

Thailand

Performing a dance from the Ramakien

GA1448

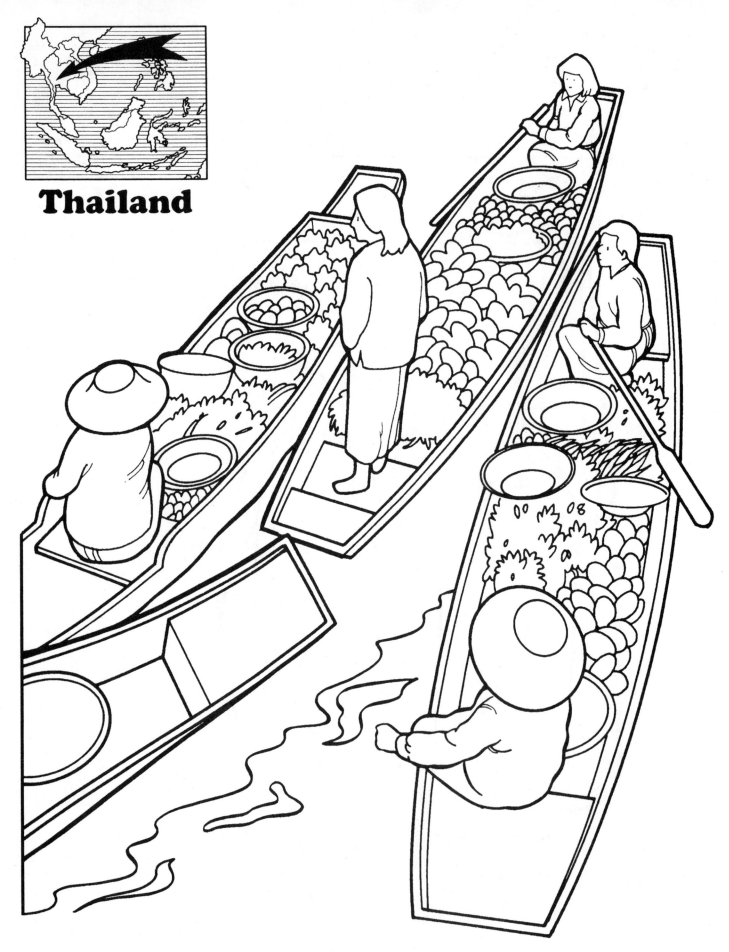

Thailand

Bangkok river market

184

Cambodia

Cambodian girls dressed for a celebration

185

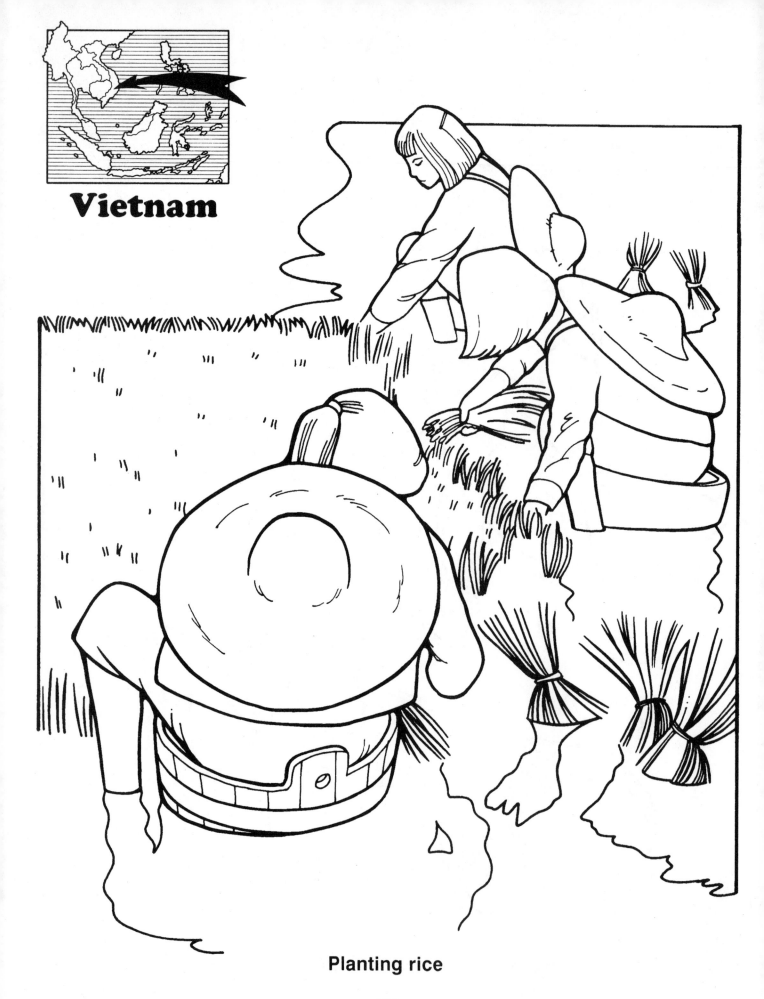

Vietnam

Planting rice

GA1448

Philippines

Sister cares for the baby as parents tend fields

187

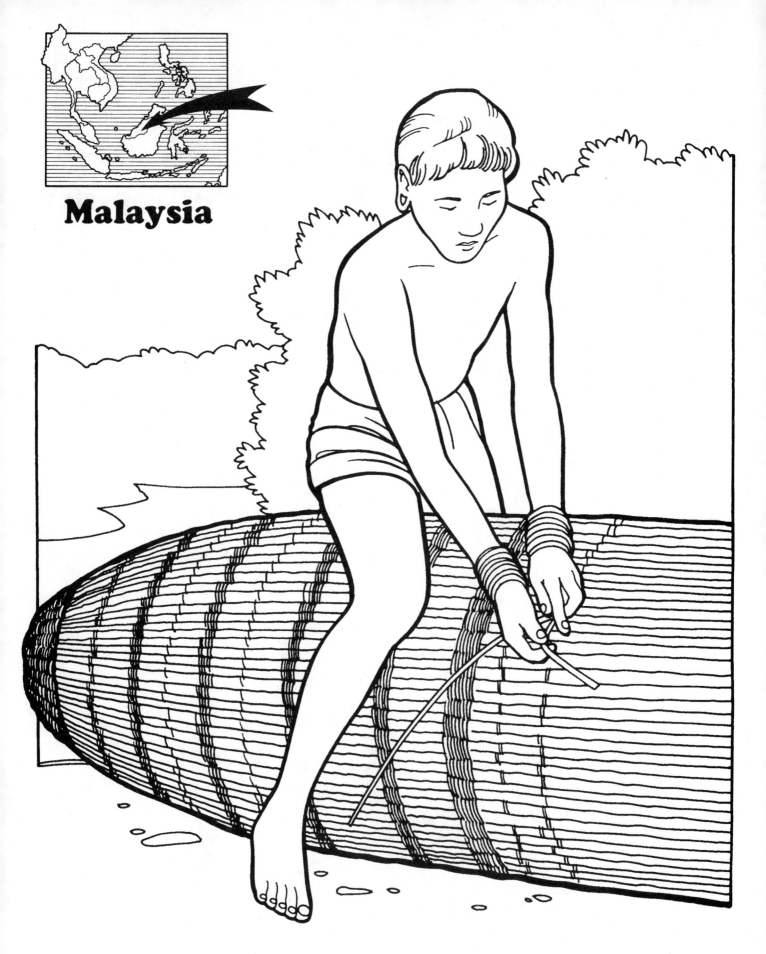

Malaysia

Iban fisherman making a fish trap

188

Indonesia

Balinese dancer

GA1448

Indonesia

Sumatran woman

190

AUSTRALIA
AND OCEANIA

191

GA1448

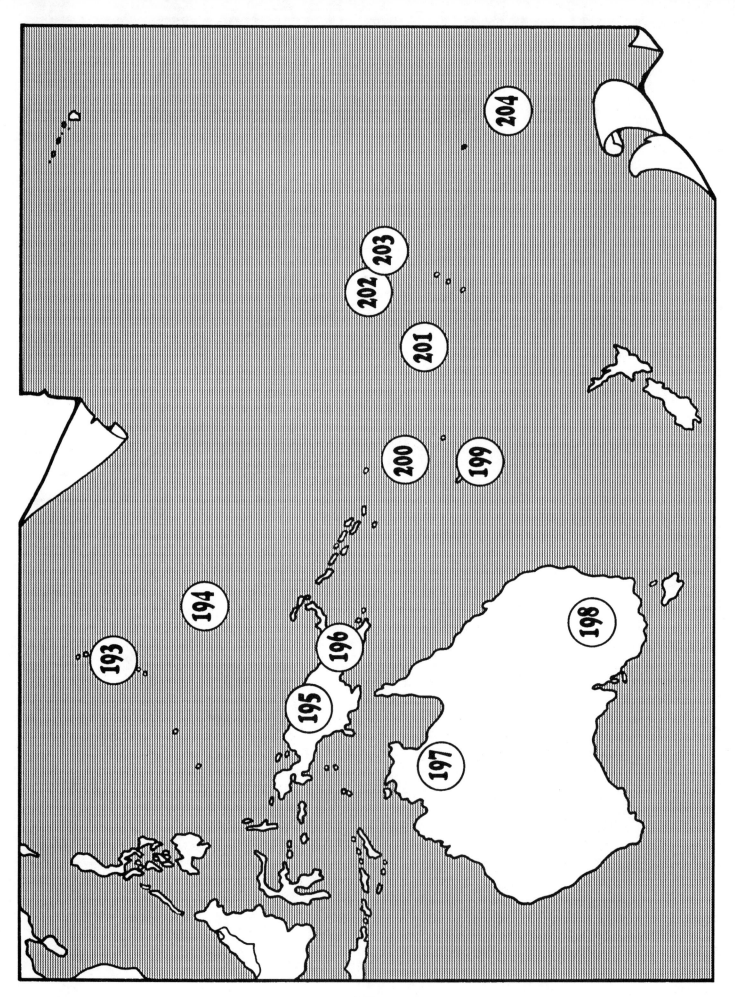

192

GA1448

Marianas

Showing off their catch

Truk

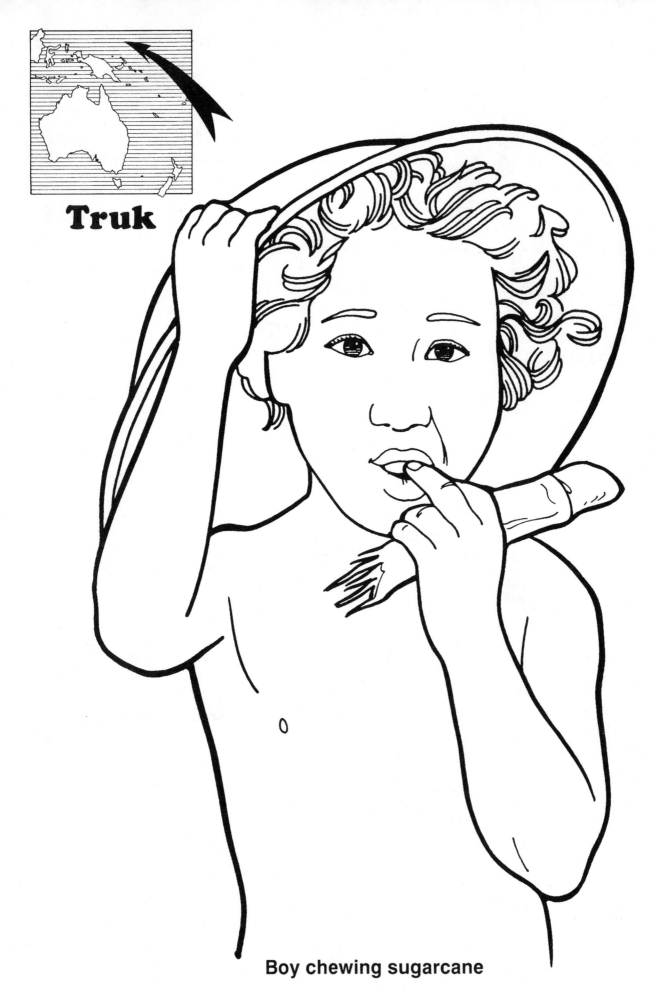

Boy chewing sugarcane

Wahgi dancer at the highlands sing-sing

New Guinea

195

New Guinea

Jale´ warrior

196

GA1448

Australia

Australian farmer

GA1448

Australia

Aborigine craftsman

198

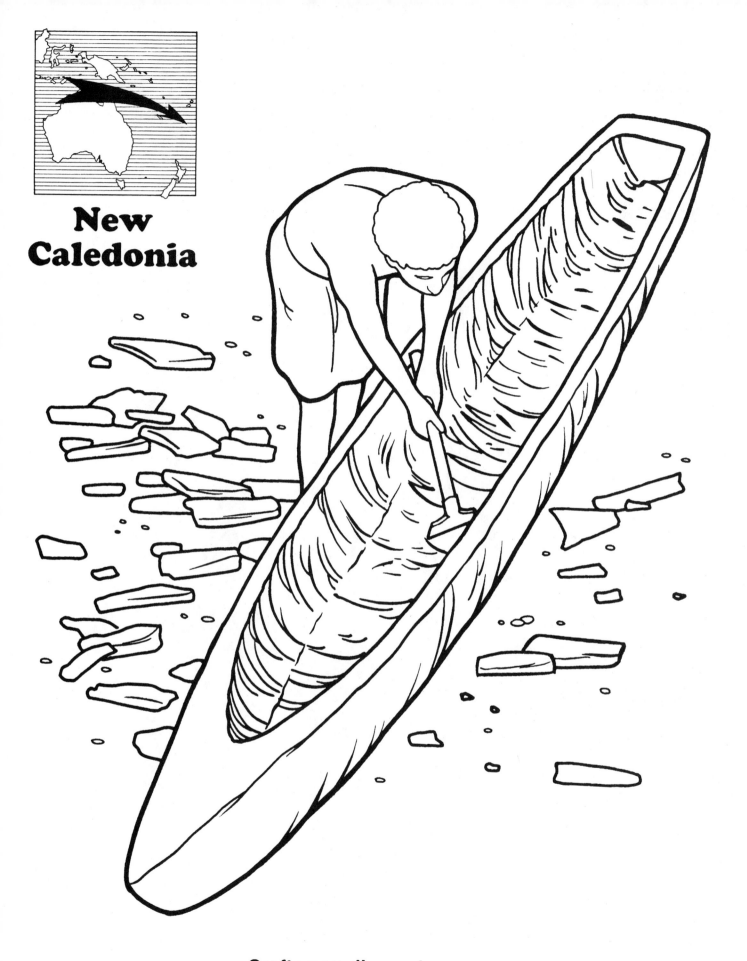

New Caledonia

Craftsman digs out a canoe

199

GA1448

New Hebrides

Ceremonial war dance

Fiji

Fijian ceremonial dance

Western Samoa

Samoan in his outrigger canoe

GA1448

American Samoa

Samoan brothers

Tahiti

Welcome dance

GA1448